CHANGING GUARD AT
BUCKINGHAM
PALACE

EGMONT
We bring stories to life

This collection first published in 2013
by Egmont UK Ltd.
The Yellow Building, 1 Nicholas Road, London W11 4AN
www.egmont.co.uk

Text by A. A. Milne copyright © Trustees of the Pooh Properties
Line illustrations copyright © E. H. Shepard
Colouring of the illustrations by Mark Burgess
copyright © 1989 Egmont UK Ltd.

ISBN 978 1 4052 6863 9

A CIP catalogue record for this title is available
from The British Library

MIX
Paper from
responsible sources
FSC www.fsc.org **FSC® C018306**

Egmont is passionate about helping to preserve the world's remaining ancient forests.
We only use paper from legal and sustainable forest sources.

This book is made from paper certified by the Forest Stewardship Council® (FSC), an organisation dedicated
to promoting responsible management of forest resources. For more information on the FSC, please visit
www.fsc.org. To learn more about Egmont's sustainable paper policy, please visit www.egmont.co.uk/ethical.

EGMONT

Our story began over a century ago, when seventeen-year-old
Egmont Harald Petersen found a coin in the street. He was on
his way to buy a flyswatter, a small hand-operated printing
machine that he then set up in his tiny apartment.

The coin brought him such good luck that today Egmont has
offices in over 30 countries around the world. And that lucky
coin is still kept at the company's head offices in Denmark.

CHANGING GUARD AT
BUCKINGHAM
PALACE

A.A.MILNE

with decorations by E.H.Shepard

EGMONT

Note

The poems in this collection have been especially selected from the two volumes of poetry on which Milne and Shepard collaborated, *Now We Are Six* and *When We Were Very Young*. They reflect the lifestyle, customs and countryside of Britain in the 1920s.

The poem *Vespers*, being in the library of the Queen's Dolls' House is printed here by special permission.

CONTENTS

BUCKINGHAM PALACE

They're changing guard at Buckingham Palace –
Christopher Robin went down with Alice.
Alice is marrying one of the guard.
'A soldier's life is terrible hard,'
                                        Says Alice.

They're changing guard at Buckingham Palace –
Christopher Robin went down with Alice.
We saw a guard in a sentry-box.
'One of the sergeants looks after their socks,'
                                        Says Alice.

They're changing guard at Buckingham Palace –
Christopher Robin went down with Alice.
We looked for the King, but he never came.
'Well, God take care of him, all the same,'
                                        Says Alice.

They're changing guard at Buckingham Palace –
Christopher Robin went down with Alice.
They've great big parties inside the grounds.
'I wouldn't be King for a hundred pounds,'

                                    Says Alice.

They're changing guard at Buckingham Palace –
Christopher Robin went down with Alice.
A face looked out, but it wasn't the King's.
'He's much too busy a-signing things,'

                                    Says Alice.

They're changing guard at Buckingham Palace –
Christopher Robin went down with Alice.
'Do you think the King knows all about *me*?'
'Sure to, dear, but it's time for tea,'

                                    Says Alice.

HAPPINESS

John had
Great Big
Waterproof
Boots on;
John had a
Great Big
Waterproof
Hat;
John had a
Great Big
Waterproof
Mackintosh –
And that
(Said John)
  Is
   That.

THE FOUR FRIENDS

Ernest was an elephant, a great big fellow,
    Leonard was a lion with a six-foot tail,
George was a goat, and his beard was yellow,
    And James was a very small snail.

Leonard had a stall, and a great big strong one,
    Ernest had a manger, and its walls were thick,
George found a pen, but I think it was the wrong one,
    And James sat down on a brick.

Ernest started trumpeting, and cracked his manger,
   Leonard started roaring, and shivered his stall,
James gave the huffle of a snail in danger
   And nobody heard him at all.

Ernest started trumpeting and raised such a rumpus,
   Leonard started roaring and trying to kick,
James went a journey with the goat's new compass
   And he reached the end of his brick.

Ernest was an elephant and very well-intentioned,
   Leonard was a lion with a brave new tail,
George was a goat, as I think I have mentioned,
   But James was only a snail.

LINES AND SQUARES

Whenever I walk in a London street,
I'm ever so careful to watch my feet;
   And I keep in the squares,
   And the masses of bears,
Who wait at the corners all ready to eat
The sillies who tread on the lines in the street,
   Go back to their lairs,
   And I say to them, 'Bears,
Just look how I'm walking in all of the squares!'

And the little bears growl to each other, 'He's mine,
As soon as he's silly and steps on a line.'
And some of the bigger bears try to pretend
That they came round the corner to look for a friend;
And they try to pretend that nobody cares
Whether you walk on the lines or squares.
But only the sillies believe their talk;
It's ever so 'portant how you walk.
And it's ever so jolly to call out, 'Bears,
Just watch me walking in all the squares!'

NURSERY CHAIRS

One of the chairs is South America,
One of the chairs is a ship at sea,
One is a cage for a great big lion,
And one is a chair for Me.

The First Chair
When I go up the Amazon,
I stop at night and fire a gun
   To call my faithful band.
And Indians in twos and threes,
Come silently between the trees,
   And wait for me to land.
And if I do not want to play
With any Indians to-day,
   I simply wave my hand.
And then they turn and go away –
   They always understand.

The Second Chair
    I'm a great big lion in my cage,
        And I often frighten Nanny with a roar.
        Then I hold her very tight, and
        Tell her not to be so frightened –
        And she doesn't be so frightened any more.

The Third Chair
    When I am in my ship, I see
      The other ships go sailing by.
    A sailor leans and calls to me
      As his tall ship goes sailing by.
    Across the sea he leans to me,
      Above the winds I hear him cry:
    'Is this the way to Round-the-World?'
      He calls as he goes by.

The Fourth Chair

Whenever I sit in a high chair
   For breakfast or dinner or tea,
I try to pretend that it's *my* chair,
   And that I am a baby of three.

Shall I go off to South America?
   Shall I put out in my ship to sea?
Or get in my cage and be lions and tigers?
Or – shall I be only Me?

DAFFODOWNDILLY

She wore her yellow sun-bonnet,
  She wore her greenest gown;
She turned to the south wind
  And curtsied up and down.
She turned to the sunlight
  And shook her yellow head,
And whispered to her neighbour:
  'Winter is dead.'

WATER-LILIES

Where the water-lilies go
To and fro,
Rocking in the ripples of the water,
Lazy on a leaf lies the Lake King's daughter,
And the faint winds shake her.
Who will come and take her?
I will! I will!
Keep still! Keep still!
Sleeping on a leaf lies the Lake King's daughter . . .
Then the wind comes skipping
To the lilies on the water;
And the kind winds wake her.
Now who will take her?
With a laugh she is slipping
Through the lilies on the water.
Wait! Wait!
Too late, too late!
Only the water-lilies go
To and fro,
Dipping, dipping,
To the ripples of the water.

THE THREE FOXES

Once upon a time there were three little foxes
Who didn't wear stockings, and they didn't wear sockses,
But they all had handkerchiefs to blow their noses,
And they kept their handkerchiefs in cardboard boxes.

They lived in the forest in three little houses,
And they didn't wear coats, and they didn't wear trousies.
They ran through the woods on their little bare tootsies,
And they played 'Touch last' with a family of mouses.

They didn't go shopping in the High Street shopses,
But caught what they wanted in the woods and copses.
They all went fishing, and they caught three wormses,
They went out hunting, and they caught three wopses.

They went to a Fair, and they all won prizes –
Three plum-puddingses and three mince-pieses.
They rode on elephants and swang on swingses,
And hit three coco-nuts at coco-nut shieses.

That's all that I know of the three little foxes
Who kept their handkerchiefs in cardboard boxes.
They lived in the forest in three little houses,
But they didn't wear coats and they didn't wear trousies.
And they didn't wear stockings and they didn't wear sockses.

DISOBEDIENCE

James James
Morrison Morrison
Weatherby George Dupree
Took great
Care of his Mother,
Though he was only three.
James James
Said to his Mother,
'Mother,' he said, said he;
'You must never go down to the end of the town,
    if you don't go down with me.'

James James
Morrison's Mother
Put on a golden gown,
James James
Morrison's Mother
Drove to the end of the town.
James James
Morrison's Mother
Said to herself, said she:
'I can get right down to the end of the town and be
    back in time for tea.'

King John
Put up a notice,
'LOST or STOLEN or STRAYED!
JAMES JAMES
MORRISON'S MOTHER
SEEMS TO HAVE BEEN MISLAID.
LAST SEEN
WANDERING VAGUELY:
QUITE OF HER OWN ACCORD,
SHE TRIED TO GET DOWN TO THE END OF
    THE TOWN – **FORTY SHILLINGS REWARD!**'

James James
Morrison Morrison
(Commonly known as Jim)
Told his
Other relations
Not to go blaming *him*.
James James
Said to his Mother,
'Mother,' he said, said he:
'You must *never* go down to the end of the town
 without consulting me.'

James James
Morrison's mother
Hasn't been heard of since.
King John
Said he was sorry,
So did the Queen and Prince.
King John
(Somebody told me)
Said to a man he knew:
'If people go down to the end of the town, well,
   what can *anyone* do?'

(*Now then, very softly*)
   J. J.
   M. M.
   W. G. Du P.
   Took great
   C/o his M*****
   Though he was only 3.
   J. J.
   Said to his M*****
   'M*****,' he said, said he:
'You-must-never-go-down-to-the-end-of-the-town-
   if-you-don't-go-down-with ME!'

THE KING'S BREAKFAST

The King asked
The Queen, and
The Queen asked
The Dairymaid:
'Could we have some butter for
The Royal slice of bread?'
The Queen asked
The Dairymaid,
The Dairymaid
Said, 'Certainly,
I'll go and tell
The cow
Now
Before she goes to bed.'

The Dairymaid
She curtsied,

And went and told
The Alderney:
'Don't forget the butter for
The Royal slice of bread.'

The Alderney
Said sleepily:
'You'd better tell
His Majesty
That many people nowadays
Like marmalade
Instead.'

The Dairymaid
Said, 'Fancy!'
And went to
Her Majesty.
She curtsied to the Queen, and
She turned a little red:
'Excuse me,
Your Majesty,
For taking of
The liberty,
But marmalade is tasty, if
It's very
Thickly
Spread.'

The Queen said,
'Oh!'
And went to
His Majesty:
'Talking of the butter for
The Royal slice of bread,
Many people
Think that
Marmalade
Is nicer.
Would you like to try a little
Marmalade
Instead?'

The King said,
'Bother!'
And then he said,
'Oh, deary me!'
The King sobbed, 'Oh, deary me!'
And went back to bed.
'Nobody,'
He whimpered,
'Could call me
A fussy man;
I *only* want
A little bit
Of butter for
My bread!'

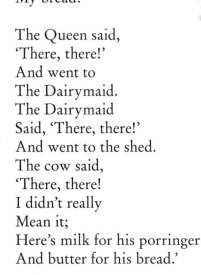

The Queen said,
'There, there!'
And went to
The Dairymaid.
The Dairymaid
Said, 'There, there!'
And went to the shed.
The cow said,
'There, there!
I didn't really
Mean it;
Here's milk for his porringer
And butter for his bread.'

The Queen took
The butter
And brought it to
His Majesty;
The King said,
'Butter, eh?'
And bounced out of bed.
'Nobody,' he said,
As he kissed her
Tenderly,
'Nobody,' he said,
As he slid down
The banisters,
'Nobody,
My darling,
Could call me
A fussy man –
BUT

I do like a little bit of butter to my bread!'

SPRING MORNING

Where am I going? I don't quite know.
Down to the stream where the king-cups grow –
Up to the hill where the pine-trees blow –
Anywhere, anywhere. *I* don't know.

Where am I going? The clouds sail by,
Little ones, baby ones, over the sky.
Where am I going? The shadows pass,
Little ones, baby ones, over the grass.
If you were a cloud, and sailed up there,

You'd sail on water as blue as air,
And you'd see me here in the fields and say:
'Doesn't the sky look green to-day?'

Where am I going? The high rooks call:
'It's awful fun to be born at all.'
Where am I going? The ring-doves coo:
'We do have beautiful things to do.'

If you were a bird, and lived on high,
You'd lean on the wind when the wind came by,
You'd say to the wind when it took you away:
'*That's* where I wanted to go to-day!'

Where am I going? I don't quite know.
What does it matter where people go?
Down to the wood where the blue-bells grow –
Anywhere, anywhere. *I* don't know.

AT THE ZOO

There are lions and roaring tigers, and enormous camels
  and things,
There are biffalo-buffalo-bisons, and a great big bear
  with wings,
There's a sort of a tiny potamus, and a tiny nosserus too –
But *I* gave buns to the elephant when I went down to
  the Zoo!

There are badgers and bidgers and bodgers, and a
  Super-in-tendent's House,
There are masses of goats, and a Polar, and different kinds
  of mouse,
And I think there's a sort of a something which is called
  a wallaboo –
But *I* gave buns to the elephant when *I* went down to
  the Zoo!

If you try to talk to the bison, he never quite
    understands;
You can't shake hands with a mingo – he doesn't like
    shaking hands.
And lions and roaring tigers *hate* saying, 'How do
    you do?'–
But I give buns to the elephant when I go down to
    the Zoo!

MISSING

Has anybody seen my mouse?

I opened his box for half a minute,
Just to make sure he was really in it,
And while I was looking, he jumped outside!
I tried to catch him, I tried, I tried . . .
I think he's somewhere about the house.
Has *anyone* seen my mouse?

Uncle John, have you seen my mouse?

Just a small sort of mouse, a dear little brown one,
He came from the country, he wasn't a town one,
So he'll feel all lonely in a London street;
Why, what could he possibly find to eat?

He must be somewhere. I'll ask Aunt Rose:
Have *you* seen a mouse with a woffelly nose?
Oh, somewhere about –
He's just got out . . .

Hasn't *anybody* seen my mouse?

AT HOME

I want a soldier
(A soldier in a busby),
I want a soldier to come and play with me.
I'd give him cream-cakes
(Big ones, sugar ones),
I'd give him cream-cakes and cream for his tea.

I want a soldier
(A tall one, a red one),
I want a soldier who plays on the drum.
Daddy's going to get one
(He's written to the shopman)
Daddy's going to get one as soon as he can come.

SUMMER AFTERNOON

Six brown cows walk down to drink
  (*All the little fishes blew bubbles at the may-fly*).
Splash goes the first as he comes to the brink,
  Swish go the tails of the five who follow . . .
Twelve brown cows bend drinking there
  (*All the little fishes went waggle-tail, waggle-tail*) –
Six from the water and six from the air;
  Up and down the river darts a blue-black swallow.

SAND-BETWEEN-THE-TOES

I went down to the shouting sea,
Taking Christopher down with me,
For Nurse had given us sixpence each –
And down we went to the beach.

We had sand in the eyes and the ears and the nose,
And sand in the hair, and sand-between-the-toes.
Whenever a good nor'-wester blows,
Christopher is certain of
Sand-between-the-toes.

The sea was galloping grey and white;
Christopher clutched his sixpence tight;
We clambered over the humping sand –
And Christopher held my hand.

We had sand in the eyes and the ears and the nose,
And sand in the hair, and sand-between-the-toes.
Whenever a good nor'-wester blows,
Christopher is certain of
Sand-between-the-toes.

There was a roaring in the sky;
The sea-gulls cried as they blew by.
We tried to talk, but had to shout –
Nobody else was out.

When we got home, we had sand in the hair,
In the eyes and the ears and everywhere;
Whenever a good nor'-wester blows,
Christopher is found with
Sand-between-the-toes.

TEDDY BEAR

A bear, however hard he tries,
Grows tubby without exercise.
Our Teddy Bear is short and fat,
Which is not to be wondered at;
He gets what exercise he can
By falling off the ottoman,
But generally seems to lack
The energy to clamber back.

Now tubbiness is just the thing
Which gets a fellow wondering;
And Teddy worried lots about
The fact that he was rather stout.
He thought: 'If only I were thin!
But how does anyone begin?'
He thought: 'It really isn't fair
To grudge me exercise and air.'

For many weeks he pressed in vain
His nose against the window-pane,
And envied those who walked about
Reducing their unwanted stout.
None of the people he could see
'Is quite' (he said) 'as fat as me!'
Then, with a still more moving sigh,
'I mean' (he said) 'as fat as I!'

Now Teddy, as was only right,
Slept in the ottoman at night,
And with him crowded in as well
More animals than I can tell;
Not only these, but books and things,
Such as a kind relation brings –
Old tales of 'Once upon a time,'
And history retold in rhyme.

One night it happened that he took
A peep at an old picture-book,
Wherein he came across by chance
The picture of a King of France
(A stoutish man) and, down below,
These words: 'King Louis So and So,
Nicknamed "The Handsome"!' There he sat,
And (think of it!) the man was fat!

Our bear rejoiced like anything
To read about this famous King,
Nicknamed 'The Handsome'. There he sat,
And certainly the man was fat.
Nicknamed 'The Handsome'. Not a doubt
The man was definitely stout.
Why then, a bear (for all his tub)
Might yet be named 'The Handsome Cub!'

'Might yet be named.' Or did he mean
That years ago he 'might have been'?
For now he felt a slight misgiving:
'Is Louis So and So still living?
Fashions in beauty have a way
Of altering from day to day.
Is "Handsome Louis" with us yet?
Unfortunately I forget.'

Next morning (nose to window-pane)
The doubt occurred to him again.
One question hammered in his head:
'Is he alive or is he dead?'
Thus, nose to pane, he pondered; but
The lattice window, loosely shut,
Swung open. With one startled 'Oh!'
Our Teddy disappeared below.

There happened to be passing by
A plump man with a twinkling eye,
Who, seeing Teddy in the street,
Raised him politely to his feet,
And murmured kindly in his ear
Soft words of comfort and of cheer:
'Well, well!' 'Allow me!' 'Not at all.'
'Tut-tut! A very nasty fall.'

Our Teddy answered not a word;
It's doubtful if he even heard.
Our bear could only look and look:
The stout man in the picture-book!
That 'handsome' King – could this be he,
This man of adiposity?
'Impossible,' he thought. 'But still,
No harm in asking. Yes I will!'

'Are you,' he said, 'by any chance
His Majesty the King of France?'
The other answered, 'I am that,'
Bowed stiffly, and removed his hat;
Then said, 'Excuse me,' with an air,
'But is it Mr Edward Bear?'
And Teddy, bending very low,
Replied politely, 'Even so!'

They stood beneath the window there,
The King and Mr Edward Bear,
And, handsome, if a trifle fat,
Talked carelessly of this and that . . .
Then said His Majesty, 'Well, well,
I must get on,' and rang the bell.
'Your bear, I think,' he smiled. 'Good-day!'
And turned, and went upon his way.

A bear, however hard he tries,
Grows tubby without exercise.
Our Teddy Bear is short and fat,
Which is not to be wondered at.
But do you think it worries him
To know that he is far from slim?
No, just the other way about –
He's *proud* of being short and stout.

KING JOHN'S CHRISTMAS

King John was not a good man –
    He had his little ways.
And sometimes no one spoke to him
    For days and days and days.
And men who came across him,
    When walking in the town,
Gave him a supercilious stare,
Or passed with noses in the air –
And bad King John stood dumbly there,
    Blushing beneath his crown.

King John was not a good man,
    And no good friends had he.
He stayed in every afternoon . . .
    But no one came to tea.
And, round about December,
    The cards upon his shelf
Which wished him lots of Christmas cheer,
And fortune in the coming year,
Were never from his near and dear,
    But only from himself.

King John was not a good man,
   Yet had his hopes and fears.
They'd given him no present now
   For years and years and years.
But every year at Christmas,
   While minstrels stood about,
Collecting tribute from the young
For all the songs they might have sung,
He stole away upstairs and hung
   A hopeful stocking out.

King John was not a good man,
   He lived his life aloof;
Alone he thought a message out
   While climbing up the roof.
He wrote it down and propped it
   Against the chimney stack:
'TO ALL AND SUNDRY – NEAR AND FAR –
F. CHRISTMAS IN PARTICULAR.'
And signed it not 'Johannes R.'
   But very humbly, 'JACK.'

'I want some crackers,
    And I want some candy;
I think a box of chocolates
    Would come in handy;
I don't mind oranges,
    I do like nuts!
And I SHOULD like a pocket-knife
    That really cuts.
And, oh! Father Christmas, if you love me at all,
Bring me a big, red india-rubber ball!'

King John was not a good man –
    He wrote this message out,
And gat him to his room again,
    Descending by the spout.
And all that night he lay there,
    A prey to hopes and fears.
'I think that's him a-coming now,'
    (Anxiety bedewed his brow.)
'He'll bring one present, anyhow –
    The first I've had for years.'

'Forget about the crackers,
    And forget about the candy;
I'm sure a box of chocolates
    Would never come in handy;
I don't like oranges,
    I don't want nuts,
And I HAVE got a pocket-knife
    That almost cuts.
But, oh! Father Christmas, if you love me at all,
Bring me a big, red india-rubber ball!'

King John was not a good man –
    Next morning when the sun
Rose up to tell a waiting world
    That Christmas had begun,
And people seized their stockings,
    And opened them with glee,
And crackers, toys and games appeared,
And lips with sticky sweets were smeared,
King John said grimly: 'As I feared,
    Nothing again for me!'

'I did want crackers,
    And I did want candy;
I know a box of chocolates
    Would come in handy;
I do love oranges,
    I did want nuts.
I haven't got a pocket-knife –
    Not one that cuts.
And, oh! if Father Christmas had loved me at all,
He would have brought a big, red india-rubber ball!'

King John stood by the window,
    And frowned to see below
The happy bands of boys and girls
    All playing in the snow.
A while he stood there watching,
    And envying them all . . .
When through the window big and red
There hurtled by his royal head,
And bounced and fell upon the bed,
    An india-rubber ball!

AND OH, FATHER CHRISTMAS,
    MY BLESSINGS ON YOU FALL
        FOR BRINGING HIM
        A BIG, RED
        INDIA-RUBBER
        BALL!

SNEEZLES

Christopher Robin
Had wheezles
And sneezles,
They bundled him
Into
His bed.
They gave him what goes
With a cold in the nose,
And some more for a cold
In the head.
They wondered
If wheezles
Could turn
Into measles,
If sneezles
Would turn
Into mumps;
They examined his chest
For a rash,

And the rest
Of his body for swellings and lumps.
They sent for some doctors
In sneezles
And wheezles
To tell them what ought
To be done.

All sorts and conditions
Of famous physicians
Came hurrying round
At a run.
They all made a note
Of the state of his throat,
They asked if he suffered from thirst;
They asked if the sneezles
Came *after* the wheezles,
Or if the first sneezle
Came first.
They said, 'If you teazle
A sneezle
Or wheezle,
A measle
May easily grow.
But humour or pleazle

The wheezle
Or sneezle,
The measle
Will certainly go.'
They expounded the reazles
For sneezles
And wheezles,
The manner of measles
When new.
They said 'If he freezles
In draughts and in breezles,
Then PHTHEEZLES
May even ensue.'

Christopher Robin
Got up in the morning,
The sneezles had vanished away.
And the look in his eye
Seemed to say to the sky,
'*Now, how to amuse them to-day?*'

BINKER

Binker – what I call him – is a secret of my own,
And Binker is the reason why I never feel alone.
Playing in the nursery, sitting on the stair,
Whatever I am busy at, Binker will be there.

> Oh, Daddy is clever, he's a clever sort of man,
> And Mummy is the best since the world began,
> And Nanny is Nanny, and I call her Nan –
>   But they can't
>   See
>   Binker.

Binker's always talking, 'cos I'm teaching him to speak:
He sometimes likes to do it in a funny sort of squeak,
And he sometimes likes to do it in a hoodling sort of roar . . .
And I have to do it for him 'cos his throat is rather sore.

Oh, Daddy is clever, he's a clever sort of man,
And Mummy knows all that anybody can.
And Nanny is Nanny, and I call her Nan –
    But they don't
    Know
    Binker.

Binker's brave as lions when we're running in the park;
Binker's brave as tigers when we're lying in the dark;
Binker's brave as elephants. He never, never cries . . .
Except (like other people) when the soap gets in his eyes.

Oh, Daddy is Daddy, he's a Daddy sort of man,
And Mummy is as Mummy as anybody can,
And Nanny is Nanny, and I call her Nan . . .
    But they're not
    Like
    Binker.

Binker isn't greedy, but he does like things to eat,
So I have to say to people when they're giving me a sweet,
'Oh, Binker wants a chocolate, so could you give me two?'
And then I eat it for him, 'cos his teeth are rather new.

Well, I'm very fond of Daddy, but he hasn't time to play,
And I'm very fond of Mummy, but she sometimes goes away,
And I'm often cross with Nanny when she wants to brush
   my hair . . .

But Binker's always Binker, and is certain to be there.

THE KNIGHT WHOSE
ARMOUR DIDN'T SQUEAK

Of all the Knights in Appledore
    The wisest was Sir Thomas Tom.
He multiplied as far as four,
    And knew what nine was taken from
To make eleven. He could write
A letter to another Knight.

No other Knight in all the land
   Could do the things which he could do.
Not only did he understand
   The way to polish swords, but knew
What remedy a Knight should seek
Whose armour had begun to squeak.

And, if he didn't fight too much,
   It wasn't that he did not care
For blips and buffetings and such,
   But felt that it was hardly fair
To risk, by frequent injuries,
A brain as delicate as his.

His castle (Castle Tom) was set
   Conveniently on a hill;
And daily, when it wasn't wet,
   He paced the battlements until
Some smaller Knight who couldn't swim
Should reach the moat and challenge him.

Or sometimes, feeling full of fight,
   He hurried out to scour the plain,
And, seeing some approaching Knight,
   He either hurried home again,
Or hid; and, when the foe was past,
Blew a triumphant trumpet-blast.

One day when good Sir Thomas Tom
    Was resting in a handy ditch,
The noises he was hiding from,
    Though very much the noises which
He'd always hidden from before,
Seemed somehow less . . . Or was it more?

The trotting horse, the trumpet's blast,
    The whistling sword, the armour's squeak,
These, and especially the last,
    Had clattered by him all the week.
Was this the same, or was it not?
Something was different. But what?

Sir Thomas raised a cautious ear
    And listened as Sir Hugh went by,
And suddenly he seemed to hear
    (Or not to hear) the reason why
This stranger made a nicer sound
Than other Knights who lived around.

Sir Thomas watched the way he went –
    His rage was such he couldn't speak,
For years they'd called him down in Kent
    The Knight Whose Armour Didn't Squeak!
Yet here and now he looked upon
Another Knight whose squeak had gone.

He rushed to where his horse was tied;
    He spurred it to a rapid trot.
The only fear he felt inside
    About his enemy was not
'How sharp his sword?' 'How stout his heart?'
But 'Has he got too long a start?'

Sir Hugh was singing, hand on hip,
    When something sudden came along,
And caught him a terrific blip
    Right in the middle of his song.

'A thunderstorm!' he thought. 'Of course!'
And toppled gently off his horse.

Then said the good Sir Thomas Tom,
    Dismounting with a friendly air,
'Allow me to extract you from
    The heavy armour that you wear.
At times like these the bravest Knight
May find his armour much too tight.'

A hundred yards or so beyond
    The scene of brave Sir Hugh's defeat
Sir Thomas found a useful pond,
    And, careful not to wet his feet,
He brought the armour to the brink,
And flung it in . . . and watched it sink.

So ever after, more and more,
  The men of Kent would proudly speak
Of Thomas Tom of Appledore,
  'The Knight Whose Armour Didn't Squeak.'
Whilst Hugh, the Knight who gave him best,
Squeaks just as badly as the rest.

BUTTERCUP DAYS

Where is Anne?
   Head above the buttercups,
Walking by the stream,
   Down among the buttercups.
Where is Anne?
Walking with her man,
Lost in a dream,
   Lost among the buttercups.
What has she got in that little brown head?
   Wonderful thoughts which can never be said.
   What has she got in that firm little fist of hers?
   Somebody's thumb, and it feels like Christopher's.
Where is Anne?
Close to her man.
Brown head, gold head,
   In and out the buttercups.

US TWO

Wherever I am, there's always Pooh,
There's always Pooh and Me.
Whatever I do, he wants to do,
'Where are you going to-day?' says Pooh:
'Well, that's very odd 'cos I was too.
'Let's go together,' says Pooh, says he.
'Let's go together,' says Pooh.

'What's twice eleven?' I said to Pooh.
('Twice what?' said Pooh to Me.)
'I *think* it ought to be twenty-two.'
'Just what I think myself,' said Pooh.
'It wasn't an easy sum to do,
But that's what it is,' said Pooh, said he.
'That's what it is,' said Pooh.

'Let's look for dragons,' I said to Pooh.
'Yes, let's,' said Pooh to Me.
We crossed the river and found a few –
'Yes, those are dragons all right,' said Pooh.
'As soon as I saw their beaks I knew.
That's what they are,' said Pooh, said he.
'That's what they are,' said Pooh.

'Let's frighten the dragons,' I said to Pooh.
'That's right,' said Pooh to Me.
'*I'm* not afraid,' I said to Pooh,
And I held his paw and shouted 'Shoo!
Silly old dragons!' – and off they flew.
'I wasn't afraid,' said Pooh, said he,
'I'm *never* afraid with you.'

So wherever I am, there's always Pooh,
There's always Pooh and Me.
'What would I do?' I said to Pooh,
'If it wasn't for you,' and Pooh said: 'True,
It isn't much fun for One, but Two
Can stick together,' says Pooh, says he.
'That's how it is,' says Pooh.

KNIGHT-IN-ARMOUR

Whenever I'm a shining Knight,
I buckle on my armour tight;
And then I look about for things,
Like Rushings-out, and Rescuings,
And Savings from the Dragon's Lair,
And fighting all the Dragons there.
And sometimes when our fights begin,
I think I'll let the Dragons win . . .
And then I think perhaps I won't,
Because they're Dragons, and I don't.

JOURNEY'S END

Christopher, Christopher, where are you going,
Christopher Robin?
'Just up to the top of the hill,
Upping and upping until
I am right on the top of the hill,'
    Said Christopher Robin.

Christopher, Christopher, why are you going,
                              Christopher Robin?
There's nothing to see, so when
You've got to the top, what then?
   'Just down to the bottom again,'
                              Said Christopher Robin.

FURRY BEAR

If I were a bear,
    And a big bear too,
I shouldn't much care
    If it froze or snew;
I shouldn't much mind
    If it snowed or friz –
I'd be all fur-lined
    With a coat like his!

For I'd have fur boots and a brown fur wrap,
And brown fur knickers and a big fur cap.
I'd have a fur muffle-ruff to cover my jaws,
And brown fur mittens on my big brown paws.
With a big brown furry-down up to my head,
I'd sleep all the winter in a big fur bed.

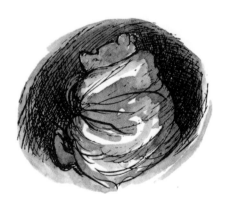

DOWN BY THE POND

I'm fishing.
Don't talk, anybody, don't come near!
Can't you see that the fish might hear?
He thinks I'm playing with a piece of string;
He thinks I'm another sort of funny sort of thing,
    But he doesn't know I'm fishing –
    He doesn't know I'm fishing.
        That's what I'm doing –
            Fishing.

No, I'm not, I'm newting.
Don't cough, anybody, don't come by!
Any small noise makes a newt feel shy.
He thinks I'm a bush, or a new sort of tree;
He thinks it's somebody, but doesn't think it's Me.
    And he doesn't know I'm newting –
    No, he doesn't know I'm newting.
      That's what I'm doing –
        Newting.

THE LITTLE BLACK HEN

Berryman and Baxter,
    Prettiboy and Penn
And old Farmer Middleton
    Are five big men . . .
And all of them were after
    The Little Black Hen.

She ran quickly,
    They ran fast;
Baxter was first, and
    Berryman was last.
I sat and watched
    By the old plum-tree . . .
She squawked through the hedge
    And she came to me.

The Little Black Hen
   Said, 'Oh, it's you!'
I said, 'Thank you,
   How do you do?
And please will you tell me,
   Little Black Hen,
What did they want,
   Those five big men?'

The Little Black Hen
   She said to me:
'They want me to lay them
   An egg for tea.
If they were Emperors,
   If they were Kings,
I'm much too busy
   To lay them things.'

'I'm not a King
   And I haven't a crown:
I climb up trees,
   And I tumble down.
I can shut one eye,
   I can count to ten,
So lay me an egg, please,
   Little Black Hen.'

The Little Black Hen said,
   'What will you pay,
If I lay you an egg
   For Easter Day?'

'I'll give you a Please
   And a How-do-you-do,
I'll show you a Bear
   Who lives in the Zoo,
I'll show you the nettle-place
   On my leg,
If you'll lay me a great big
Eastery egg.'

The Little Black Hen
　　Said, 'I don't care
For a How-do-you-do
　　Or a Big-brown-bear,
But I'll lay you a beautiful
　　Eastery egg,
If you'll show me the nettle-place
　　On your leg.'

I showed her the place
　　Where I had my sting.
She touched it gently
　　With one black wing.
'Nettles don't hurt
　　If you count to ten.
And now for the egg,'
　　Said the Little Black Hen.

When I wake up
　　On Easter Day,
I shall see my egg
　　She's promised to lay.
If I were Emperors,
　　If I were Kings,
It couldn't be fuller
Of wonderful things.

Berryman and Baxter,
 Prettiboy and Penn,
And old Farmer Middleton
 Are five big men.
All of them are wanting
 An egg for their tea,
But the Little Black Hen is much too busy,
The Little Black Hen is *much* too busy,
The Little Black Hen is MUCH too busy . . .
 She's laying my egg for me!

THE FRIEND

There are lots and lots of people who are always asking
    things,
Like Dates and Pounds-and-ounces and the names of funny
    Kings,
And the answer's either Sixpence or A Hundred Inches
    Long,
And I know they'll think me silly if I get the answer
    wrong.

So Pooh and I go whispering, and Pooh looks very bright,
And says, 'Well, *I* say sixpence, but I don't suppose I'm
    right.'
And then it doesn't matter what the answer ought to be,
'Cos if he's right, I'm Right, and if he's wrong, it isn't Me.

THE GOOD LITTLE GIRL

It's funny how often they say to me, 'Jane?
   'Have you been a *good* girl?'
   'Have you been a *good* girl?'
And when they have said it, they say it again,
   'Have you been a *good* girl?'
   'Have you been a *good* girl?'

I go to a party, I go out to tea,
I go to an aunt for a week at the sea,
I come back from school or from playing a
   game;
Wherever I come from, it's always the same:
   'Well?
Have you been a *good* girl, Jane?'

It's always the end of the loveliest day:
  'Have you been a *good* girl?'
  'Have you been a *good* girl?'
I went to the Zoo, and they waited to say:
  'Have you been a *good* girl?'
  'Have you been a *good* girl?'

Well, what did they think that I went there to do?
And why should I want to be bad at the Zoo?
And should I be likely to say if I had?
So that's why it's funny of Mummy and Dad,
This asking and asking, in case I was bad,
  'Well?
Have you been a *good* girl, Jane?'

THE MORNING WALK

When Anne and I go out for a walk,
We hold each other's hand and talk
Of all the things we mean to do
When Anne and I are forty-two.

And when we've thought about a thing,
Like bowling hoops or bicycling,
Or falling down on Anne's balloon,
We do it in the afternoon.

EXPLAINED

Elizabeth Ann
Said to her Nan:
'Please will you tell me how God began?
Somebody must have made Him. So
Who could it be, 'cos I want to know?'
And Nurse said, '*Well!*'
And Ann said, 'Well?
I know you know, and I wish you'd tell.'
And Nurse took pins from her mouth, and said,
'Now then, darling, it's time for bed.'

Elizabeth Ann
Had a wonderful plan:
She would run round the world till she found a man
Who knew *exactly* how God began.

She got up early, she dressed, and ran
Trying to find an Important Man.
She ran to London and knocked at the door
Of the Lord High Doodelum's coach-and-four.
'Please, sir (if there's anyone in),
However-and-ever did God begin?'

The Lord High Doodelum lay in bed

But out of the window, large and red,
Came the Lord High Coachman's face instead.
And the Lord High Coachman laughed and said:
'Well, what put *that* in your quaint little head?'

Elizabeth Ann went home again
And took from the ottoman Jennifer Jane.
'Jenniferjane,' said Elizabeth Ann,
'Tell me *at once* how God began.'
And Jane, who didn't much care for speaking,
Replied in her usual way by squeaking.

What did it mean? Well, to be quite candid,
I don't know, but Elizabeth Ann did.
Elizabeth Ann said softly, 'Oh!
Thank you, Jennifer. Now I know.'

FORGOTTEN

Lords of the Nursery
    Wait in a row,
Five on the high wall,
    And four on the low;
Big Kings and Little Kings,
    Brown Bears and Black,
All of them waiting
    Till John comes back.

Some think that John boy
    Is lost in the wood,
Some say he couldn't be,
    Some say he could.
Some think that John boy
    Hides on the hill;
Some say he won't come back,
    Some say he will.

High was the sun, when
   John went away . . .
Here they've been waiting
   All through the day;
Big Bears and Little Bears,
   White Kings and Black,
All of them waiting
   Till John comes back.

Lords of the Nursery
   Looked down the hill,
Some saw the sheep-fold,
   Some saw the mill;
Some saw the roofs
   Of the little grey town . . .
And their shadows grew long
   As the sun slipt down.

Gold between the poplars
    An old moon shows;
Silver up the star-way
    The full moon rose;
Silver down the star-way
    The old moon crept . . .
And, one by another,
    The grey fields slept.

Lords of the Nursery
    Their still watch keep . . .
They hear from the sheep-fold
    The rustle of sheep.
A young bird twitters
    And hides its head;
A little wind suddenly
    Breathes, and is dead.

Slowly and slowly
    Dawns the new day . . .
What's become of John boy?
    No one can say.
Some think that John boy
    Is lost on the hill;
Some say he won't come back,
    Some say he will.

What's become of John boy?
　　Nothing at all,
He played with his skipping rope,
　　He played with his ball.
He ran after butterflies,
　　Blue ones and red;
He did a hundred happy things –
　　And then went to bed.

IN THE DARK

I've had my supper,
  And *had* my supper,
    And *HAD* my supper and all;
I've heard the story
  Of Cinderella,
    And how she went to the ball;
I've cleaned my teeth,
  And I've said my prayers,
    And I've cleaned and said them right;
And they've all of them been
  And kissed me lots,
    They've all of them said 'Good-night.'

So – here I am in the dark alone,
  There's nobody here to see;

I think to myself,
   I play to myself,
 And nobody knows what I say to myself;
Here I am in the dark alone,
   What is it going to be?
I can think whatever I like to think,
I can play whatever I like to play,
I can laugh whatever I like to laugh,
   There's nobody here but me.

I'm talking to a rabbit . . .

I'm talking to the sun . . .
I think I am a hundred –
  I'm one.
I'm lying in a forest . . .
  I'm lying in a cave . . .
I'm talking to a Dragon . . .
  I'm BRAVE.
I'm lying on my left side . . .
  I'm lying on my right . . .
I'll play a lot to-morrow . . .

    . . . . . .

I'll think a lot to-morrow . . .

    . . . . . .

I'll laugh . . .
      a lot . . .
         to-morrow . . .
      (*Heigh-ho!*)
            Good-night.

THE END

When I was One,
I had just begun.

When I was Two,
I was nearly new.

When I was Three,
I was hardly Me.

When I was Four,
I was not much more.

When I was Five,
I was just alive.

But now I am Six, I'm as clever as clever.
So I think I'll be six now for ever and ever.

VESPERS

Little Boy kneels at the foot of the bed,
Droops on the little hands little gold head.
Hush! Hush! Whisper who dares!
Christopher Robin is saying his prayers.

God bless Mummy. I know that's right.
Wasn't it fun in the bath to-night?
The cold's so cold, and the hot's so hot.
Oh! *God bless Daddy* – I quite forgot.

If I open my fingers a little bit more,
I can see Nanny's dressing-gown on the door.
It's a beautiful blue, but it hasn't a hood.
Oh! *God bless Nanny and make her good.*

Mine has a hood, and I lie in bed,
And pull the hood right over my head,
And I shut my eyes, and I curl up small,
And nobody knows that I'm there at all.

Oh! *Thank you, God, for a lovely day.*
And what was the other I had to say?
I said 'Bless Daddy,' so what can it be?
Oh! Now I remember it. *God bless Me.*

Little Boy kneels at the foot of the bed,
Droops on the little hands little gold head.
Hush! Hush! Whisper who dares!
Christopher Robin is saying his prayers.